FROM THE
BEATING HEART
OF Healing

PHYSICIAN / PATIENT BONDS
THROUGH THE POETRY OF

Jan Thatcher Adams MD

First Printing September 2020

ISBN: 978-057876564-8

Cover design by Roslyn McFarland with Far Lands Publishing

Dances On High Publishing

"Dr. Jan Adams' splendid poetry emerges from the empathy, compassion, and skills of a great physician. In our increasingly technical age, we need to be reminded of what the heart of healing is, and has always been, about. This is that reminder."
—Larry Dossey, MD, Author: *One Mind: How Our Individual Mind Is Part of a Greater Consciousness and Why It Matters*

"Wow, Jan, congratulations! You are a master storyteller. You have written a beautiful book that brought tears to my eyes and chuckles to my heart. Each story is poignant, fascinating, and incredibly real. I don't know about most people, but I know that every single nurse and doctor will absolutely say that you are telling their story. The stories are SO REAL that they filled up my heart. Thank you - you fabulous storyteller - for gifting all of us with your knowledge, wisdom, and beautiful heart. You are the Mark Twain of medicine!!"
—Bill Manahan, MD, Co-Chair Minnesota Holistic Medicine Group, Assistant Professor Emeritus, Department of Family Medicine, University of Minnesota, Author of *Eat For Health: A Do-It-Yourself Nutrition Guide for Solving Common Medical Problems*

"Your poetic words explode with pithy meaning. Jan's succinct, close to the heart observations elicit an emotional response that we here-to-fore may not have considered; it brings the reader to a new level of consciousness. A must have book that reflects a new way of seeing."
—Lynn Keegan, PhD, RN, AHN-BC, FAAN, Explorer-Educator-Author, *Holistic Nursing: A Handbook for Practice,* Barbara Montgomery Dossey and Lynn Keegan

"Dr, Jan T. Adams lays out a cornucopia for the soul. She is a physician who leans in and listens with an open heart and reverence for the journey of life of each of her patients. In doing so, she becomes more than the doctor, she becomes "medicine." She then transforms the suffering and awe of what she carries from her office into the luminous prose/poetry you hold in your hands. She marks each of these patient's journeys as important and holds each soul tenderly in her hands, so that you too might experience the human condition with new eyes. If you are a health-care provider, you may see a way forward, a way to stay human and survive the mind-numbing grind of managed care. Discover your own way to creatively care enough for yourself and your patients to do as Jan has done, by looking deeply and loving wisely enough to give voice to it all. As each story excavates the life she has been privileged to witness, we watch her tenderly hold each in her competent and caring hands and heart. A must read for physicians-to-be, those that need to be re-inspired, and for consumers alike.

—Lora DeVore-Matz, M.S., LICSW and writer of the book, *Fishing for Fallen Light* coming out late next year. I have had the profound, life-changing privilege of being both a patient of Dr. Jan as well as a mentee many years ago. She is rare individual who intuitively practices the art of medicine and in doing so is a true healer.

DEDICATION

To my one and only Deemster

ACKNOWLEDGEMENTS

I have enjoyed a most privileged life as a woman doctor and healer, beginning at a time when very few women were allowed in medical school. Medicine was then and forever my first love for an occupation. I am deeply grateful for the opportunity to be in this field, and extend the most special thanks to the thousands of individuals and families who invited me into their healing process and stories. And strong recognition goes to the hundreds of staff whose dedication allowed me to do my work-especially Paula. Now, age snuck up on me and made retirement reluctantly necessary. But no matter what difficulties I meet as time dwindles, I shall always call upon the great good gifts of this amazing career for meaning and comfort.

Also, enormous thanks to Heidi Hansen and Linda B. Myers for their relentless encouragement and remarkable help in organizing and publishing this book.

Many of the poems in this book have appeared *In The Words of Olympic Peninsula Authors* anthologies.

CONTENTS

TROY

Hundreds of teenagers
pass through the clinic this night,
with athletic physical form,
and urine bottle in hand.

I examine Troy, who like many
voice-changing young men,
finds his body erect,
in embarrassing ways
out of his control.

I know his discomfort,
and keep up steady
conversation as a distraction for him.

Later, I sit in my office,
adjacent to the waiting room,
and I overhear Troy
instructing a peer.

"First a nurse takes your
blood pressure and weighs
and measures you.
Then, you have to go piss in a bottle.
Then she puts you in a room and tells
you to strip to your shorts.

Then, you HOPE TO GOD
a **woman** doesn't come in!"

I never have to wait long
for the next smile to happen.

AUDREY

"Heart medicine is expensive —
I'm out of work.
So I went off it.
Yes, I started smoking again."

So, in hundred-degree heat,
and no air conditioning,
the pain starts again,
gnawing
with insistent
dullard's teeth
inside her
chest.

For two days she resists that message.
After all, one nitroglycerin relieves
the pain
each time.

Finally, remembering last year's
heart attack
and
balloon angioplasty,
Audrey visits me at my office.
She is fifty-one.

I hear her story,
see her fear and her color,
and send her directly to
the coronary care unit,
where an EKG confirms
an impending
heart attack.

A few hours later, her
heart
stops.

Because she is in coronary care,
help is immediate —
she is rescued.

The next morning,
on her way to
angiography,

I take her hand and tell her
there are often samples of
her heart medicine at my clinic.
If she cannot afford it,
I will give her those.

As to the smoking,
she seems prepared to stop.
But I know even as sure death curls
upward and inward on that seductive smoke,
its tendril grip, like some glorious, flowering,
choking vine,
may be too strong to deny.

BRENDA

Chart in hand,
I open the next door.
The stench assaults me.
I struggle to maintain
a compassionate face.

But the young woman seems healthy,
her cheeks rosy, her body alive.

"The discharge started a week ago. It's unbearable!
I cannot go anywhere. It's as if there's another,
rotten person beside me every moment."

I expect to find a forgotten tampon —
this odor is reminiscent.
But when I explore, I realize
Brenda's sexual partner
is in major trouble.
Hidden deeply there, in putrid glory,
sits a medium onion.

I do not know if it's Bermuda or Vidalia.

JESSE

I know he will,
with some coaxing,
smile a great blossoming peony
of a smile.

This will cause me joy, and will, as well
reassure me that, at two months,
he can see,
probably can hear,
has normal neurological development, and most likely is
well-cared for.

But first I have to distract him
from staring, fascinated and following,
at the fluorescent lights that line one end of the ceiling.

And I know that, after his smile,
his moth-gaze will drift back
to that irresistible light.

In this activity,
he is like all babies his age.

I have been taught this
attraction to light occurs
because the brightness
penetrates still-fuzzy vision.

But I believe he follows
the light
because it is what he remembers best
in his
NEWBORN ANCIENT SPIRIT.

TRISH

Sure, she'd noticed a slight
thickening at the waist —
but pregnancy? Impossible!
Certainly not due in less than a month.

Her body — wiry, muscled,
colorfully tattooed
from neck to ankles,
tensed at my diagnosis.

No way! No way! No way!

Denial is a powerful thing,
to hide the insistent
thumping of a near term
baby from its mother's
awareness.

No birth control for ten years —
"I cannot get pregnant."

But there you are,
nonetheless, due in one month.

At term, a lusty infant boy
arrived on cue,
And she cuddled
the child, though
remained amazed.

Today, I read my mail.
A letter from an Emergency Room.
She has been punched in the face,
and pushed, twice, from a moving vehicle,
by her husband.

The infant, folded in her arms
like a football, escaped harm.
The letter tells me the child was bloody,
though it proved to be
only
Trish's
blood.

No, she will not press charges,
she insisted, with beery breath,
through freshly missing teeth.
"I'm a big girl,
I can take care of myself."

Babies and tattooed women,
thrown from moving cars —
despair
and denial,
come bound in
multicolored
packages.

TRAVIS

Today I am weary —
emergency calls
robbed sleep last night.
And personal issues knot
tangled weights in
my shoulders and neck.

With sighing spirit I
enter yet another exam room.
There Travis and his mom,
new to my clinic,
await help for his painful ear.

As I examine and touch,
he and I talk of sand-box concerns —
his puppy, swimming lessons,
his favorite toy,
the suckers in my pocket.

Finished, I write a prescription,
while Travis turns with earnest face
to his mom.

"Mom, is she an angel?"

Surprised, I search mom's face.
She shrugs -
she does not know the source of this question.

I leave the room —
unburdened.

ADAM

At forty-two,
no one expects
the sudden swift blow
of a heart attack.
True, Adam's dad
died young
of heart problems.

But mortality is not
on Adam's mind
this day.

In coronary care,
he's still digesting
his diagnosis, when
cardiac arrest
slices
through his stability.

I come quickly,
my home only
five
dusty
minutes
away.

I work with my tools —
medicines,
shock,
CPR.

Forty-five minutes later,
his reluctant heart
begins a thready,
then strong
water-drum calypso.

Next day, he asks
to speak privately.
Verbatim, he repeats all my words and actions during
the arrest.

And I understand —
He has experienced that tunnel,
that white light.

I ask for details,
he refuses, but says

"I want you to know
now,
I am not afraid to die."

The next day he again
slides into that
illuminated darkness.
I am unable to revive him.

But I often thank him
for that gift.

LUCY

It was a simple cold,
but now is clearly
more complicated,
with severe cough,
fever, green mucous.

X-rays confirm
the pneumonia.
I will treat with antibiotics.

I ask Lucy to also take acidophilus,
to counter some of
antibiotic's side effects.

I see her puzzle at this,
and ask if she knows
about acidophilus.

She brightens in her fever,
and says,
"Isn't that a
Greek philosopher?"

We both laugh.
I know she will not
be ill for long.

JODY FOURTEEN YEARS

Her father, wearing
only a towel,
met the public health nurse
at the door,
and lounged,
lewdly.

Perhaps he was not
the father/grandfather
of the twins
Jody so grumpily carried
in her bursting belly.
She never said,
but I wondered.

Her mother, struck
in rusty iron
from some classic
victim mode,
stopped me
at the hospital door one day,
begging for $300 to buy a car.

Soon I will deliver these identical twin girls —
to grow up hearing what words?
Seeing what actions?
Receiving what blows?

These thoughts I must release.
Instead I shall,
when I can,
squeeze these babies
kind and warm.

JODY TWENTY-ONE YEARS

The twins,
pretty, blonde,
seven years wild,
add to the commotion in
my exam room,
made crowded by their
mother, her hostile,
tattooed boyfriend, and
their wailing toddler.

In Jody, now,
I see some maturing,
some slight spark,
smoldering feeble
for lack of oxygen.

Today, she fears she is
once again pregnant.
Tests confirm.

Amid the clatter and clamber,
I find, on exam,
The beginnings
of miscarriage.

There
are
no
tears.

SAMANTHA

Maybe it was the full moon —
no one ever really knew
what made the gunman shoot
a high-powered rifle repeatedly
into a crowded bar and dance hall.

In the Emergency Room, with sixteen
wounded and four dead,
I attend first one lifeless young woman,
one side of her neck missing,
then another young woman,
the bullets in her brain
snuffing her sparkle and breath.

But Samantha is luckier.
Her right breast, swollen
and dusky like
a bruised melon,
contains fourteen
pieces of shrapnel.

She refuses surgery,
terrified her husband will
discover her evening out
with another man.

I leave the room for a moment,
to decide if I can handle this much metal
without a trip
to the operating room.

When I return, she
is gone, slipped with
her guilt into the
ambulance-loud summer night.

Whatever became of Samantha,
with the melon-bruise breast?
The lucky one that did not die.
I doubt if that cheating metal
went long without detection.

TIMOTHY

Though only forty-five, the chest pain
sounded worrisome,
like an impending heart attack.

Normally, I would admit Timothy
into the local coronary care unit,
for observation.
Listening to that insistent
quiet intuition, though,
I instead send him to a larger hospital,
with cardiac surgery capabilities.

There, they observe him and prepare,
after two uneventful days,
to send him home.
As he stands at the desk
receiving discharge instructions, he
suddenly collapses in full cardiac arrest.

He is immediately revived and
rushed to surgery,
where four offending clogged vessels
are bypassed.

Many of us would likely take great
note of such a near fatal event,
and change our lives accordingly.

Timothy, though, doesn't seem able to act
on these urgent challenges.

He continues to ignore his
insulin dependent diabetes,
to drink too much alcohol,
to eat far too much, to smoke,
and to exercise not at all.

His wife divorced him, and his diet worsened.
Now, ten years later, he presents himself,
once again in serious trouble with his heart.

This time, the heart muscle is failing,
his blood pressure is outrageously high,
he is drowning in retained fluid, and
he must decide whether he will live or die.

In intensive care, he loses twenty pounds
of choking fluid,
and breathes much easier.
I am blunt with him, and ask
if there is anything worth living for,
or anything left he wishes to do
with his life.
If so, he must change,
and change now.

He is earnest, frightened.
He begins cardiac rehab.
stops smoking, loses more weight,
exercises, controls his diabetes.
He feels well and looks good.

But slowly, over several months,
the old grip of lethal habits
tightens again. A last try with antidepressant
medicine makes no difference.
New gains slide away, and I see
I will need to assure him
I will not leave as his physician, even though
his choice is early death.

What are those secrets he locks
so tightly in closed heart — those
hidden events that froze his spirit into
purchasing sure and swift death?
What is the pain this life brought,
so unbearable as to need respite in the grave?

I will never know — Timothy is not talking.
I must just accept the power
of the human will to decide
between life or death,
for its own compelling reasons.
And I leave my hand open
and accepting.

THOMAS

Before colonoscopy was
the screening for colon cancer,
We doctors provided a draconian procedure
called proctoscopy.

The proctoscope, a fourteen-inch-long steel tube, inflexible.
The examination — painful, done without sedatives,
on the bottom of my
favorites in procedures.

Even so, it was needed.
So, Thomas presents himself,
after a long night of fun with laxatives.
To finish his prep, my nurse hands him
two Fleet enemas.
She shows him to the bathroom.

My gleaming torture instrument awaits him
And waits
And waits
And waits.

Finally, my nurse knocks on the bathroom door.
"Is everything ok?"

"Well," he says," I drank both of them
but nothing is happening!"

Lucky man!
He has to reschedule his torture!

CHARLES

He was small, elderly, grumpy, crude and rude.
He abused the nurses verbally and with his cane.
His nightly 2:00 AM ambulance to ER visits
never varied.

"I can't sleep, my back hurts, I haven't pooped
For five days!
Give me that fucking shot, now!"
All attempts to divert him to non-narcotic
medicines failed. His demands would be met,
or he would not go home.
All information supplied him regarding the dangers of his
escalating narcotic use and constipation problems
went unheeded.

One morning I arrived
for morning hospital rounds
to find him admitted,
with multiple enema treatments under way.

My examination revealed
an ominously hard, swollen belly,
with no bowel sounds.
I knew immediately he
was on his last narcotic mission.

CT scan confirmed his ruptured bowel,
his abdomen filled with foul fluid.
Surgery was his only hope,
and likely to be the final event
of his miserable, frail existence.

The surgery was a success.
Some days later, Charles died.
Sometimes, a strong and
abusive personality
leads to fatal consequences.

FRANKIE

Here he is again.
It is his monthly ER visit
for tooth pain.

At twenty-six, his mouth is filled with black rotting
and cracked stumps for teeth.
This is the result of his relentless
Meth habit.

He has braved the deep snow and bitter cold,
walking in the dawn hours from
his homeless shelter.

He is praying the doctor in the ER
will give him oxy's for his tooth pain —
Of course it says right there on his chart
he is allergic to all narcotics, Tylenol, and ibuprofen —
except OxyContin. This is the drug he can sell on the street
to get more meth.

He does not go to the dentist —
despite the free clinic info
we provide him each month.
Tooth repair is not his goal.

It is a bad day for him.
He got me for his doctor.

I write him a prescription for antibiotic
to clean up his mouth.
No oxy
He is angry.

As I am leaving the room,
he turns and
pees on the back wall of his exam room.

I do not comment.
Instead, I remind myself —
I have all his luck!

LARA AND TONYA

They are beautiful children, ages five and seven.
Their illnesses — mild colds.
They have a history of ear infection,
so mom brought them in.
Curly long hair, mischievous laughs,
and cheerful smiles inform me they are not
in serious medical trouble.
I notice their Russian names.
"Mom, are you Russian?" I ask.
Five-year-old Lara interjects, "No.
Mom loves Dr. Chicago!"
I never know where the next laugh will arise,
But I know for certain it will be healing.

POLLY

A charming, mischievous toddler,
she brings me shredded toilet paper
from the adjacent room
and cavorts about as
her mom and I talk.

Polly had a brief low fever
two hours earlier
but it is gone now.
She also got a nasal flu dose today,
as her sister has influenza.
Although late, her mom
decided to immunize her for the season.

She has no cough
or vomit
or diarrhea.

I examine her.
She is completely normal.
A lively, delightful little person.

Two days later I return to this hospital site.
All the staff is watching me.
Something is wrong.

One day after I saw Polly,
an ambulance screamed in
with her in extremis.
Her seizing little body
unalert, frothing at the mouth.

The doctor could not save her.
The entire hospital grieved
and attended her funeral.

Influenza — double dose
from her sister and also the too-late immunization
killed her, according to the pathologist.

Nothing in life is guaranteed,
not even that bright little charmers
will live to beguile another day.

SAM

His tummy waged war,
with steady cramps, vomit, and diarrhea.
He fell from toilet to floor,
in a sweaty faint.

Shortly, he awoke to his dog
licking his behind.

Later, In the Emergency room,
I said,
"Now that's a real service dog!"

With much laughter,
we all set about his healing.

JACK

Schizophrenia is a chameleon
chewing on its victims in relentless torture,
especially when medications are tossed out.

Jack, brought to the ER by police,
is violently paranoid and hallucinating.
He is shouting disconnected words and thoughts,
and hitting, kicking, biting
all who try to bring him some relief.

He must be restrained for a time,
and provided a critical injection
to calm his inflamed mind and body.

It works — he is so tired.
He sleeps, out of restraints.
He wakes and devours a meal.

Though closely observed,
he suddenly strips and
sprints, buck naked,
into another department,
seriously alarming a raft
of patients and nurses.

Security attempts to corral him,
but, with a stunned audience,
he just flops on his back and spread-eagles
on the cool floor.

Eventually four strong men,
each lifting a rigid limb,
manage to muscle this wild, naked man
back to the ER, for restraints and another shot,
leaving a trail of folks behind who will
sure have something to discuss
over dinner.

As for Jack, he will spend
the next many weeks,
locked somewhere in a psych ward,
getting back on his medicines.

They say schizophrenia "burns out"
when its victims age past sixty or seventy.
Until then, this stricken young man
will rage, rage against the
Merciless Voices
in his brain.

JOSEPH'S HEART

It was his third heart attack.
At 89, he knew his time grew short.
there remained no further surgeries,
medicines, or stents
that could help.

Today is Friday,
and his wildly beating heart
is keeping me and the staff busy
with treatment.

But, he has a full family reunion tomorrow,
and he is pleading to go.
I repeatedly tell him
his heart will not allow it.

Finally, he says
"I'd rather die of a heart attack
Than a broken heart!"

I heard that message.
I explain to him how to
Sign Out Against Medical Advice
in the morning,
and we agree on ways
for him to rest and minimize
the chance of disaster.

Three weeks later I return to
This hospital for more shifts.
I am thrilled to see him in the clinic,
terrible shape as usual,
regaling me with stories from
this, his last earthly reunion.

The heart speaks
a strong language,
and must be heard.

GRETA

In the tight aisle airline seat,
I am across from an elderly lady.

The flight attendant brings boiling hot coffee,
and it spills in Greta's lap.

I am up immediately to help.
We all proceed quickly to the rear of the plane.

Poor Greta is whimpering.
We remove her steaming garments,
to find her lower abdomen, private parts,
and upper legs already blistered.

Ice is applied, and cool moist rags,
with some relief.
Pain medicine is available in the flight bag,
and that helps.

She is awkwardly lying on the crowded floor,
exposed.
A kind flight attendant
provides her own dry clothes for cover,
after we loosely swaddle the entire area
with salve and bandages.

She is taken to first class where she can stretch out.
An ambulance meets the plane when we arrive.

Travel disaster —
a risk one takes.

GRACE

Her mother, knowing she could not beat
the terrible heroin and crack cocaine habit,
decided on abortion.
She went to an agency, where the nice lady
told her the pregnancy was from the grace of god,
and the child would be God's child.

The agency did not have the ability
to help with health,
but they provided some diaper coupons
and several nice pamphlets complimenting
her mother on deciding for life.
So, with no prenatal care, her mom birthed Grace
on the floor of a filthy crack house, barely aware
she was
bleeding to death.

Grace lived in an incubator for two months,
as she painfully withdrew from her drug addiction,
and gained the weight she had not in utero,
due to malnutrition.

Adopted at age two by my patient,
who had a lovely little girl already
and wanted to help this sweet unfortunate child,
Grace seemed charming and delightful.

At age four Grace set her sister on fire.
Sister survived, with horrible burns.
When six, Grace burned the shed
and stabbed the family dog.

The counselors diagnosed her a psychopath.
She was remanded to institutionalization
until age eighteen.
Her parents unadopted her,
breaking under the financial burden of her care.

At twenty she coldly killed a fellow heroin addict,
who had a syringe she wanted.
Through all of this,
where was the nice lady
from the agency
who made sure this gift from God
graced the earth?

ALMA

She was a feisty ninety-four,
lived right across the street from
my clinic.

She and her husband
emigrated from Russia, and
she was a piano teacher
until her mid-eighties.

She saw me once a year,
grudgingly.
She called herself
"Just an old vitch!"

As a family doc, I was privileged to care for her,
her elderly husband,
her daughter and grandchildren.

One day she came for her yearly visit.
She was not on medications and had no complaints.
Her examination was unremarkable
for her advanced age.

She surprised me by asking
If she had heard correctly
from friends that I play the piano and organ.

I affirmed that,
then she stunned me by
removing a large pile of Russian piano music
from her bag.

When she presented it to me, she said-
"This is for you. I won't need it anymore,
But you will, you'll see."

That night, she died in her sleep.

She never learned that I
became so involved with Russia
and its culture, I married a Russian man.

He very much enjoys the
music she gifted me.

WAYNE

Urgent pleas for a doctor
wake me from my uncomfortable
airline cramped sleep.

At the rear service deck,
I find a ridiculously drunken man
worried about his headache
and soaring blood pressure.

He has forgotten to take his medicine
and now he is in trouble.
I have him lie down,
a pillow under his red-faced head.
The flight attendant retrieves his carry-on.

I find his medication, and administer a double dose.
A cool cloth to his forehead calms him.
Soon, he sleeps
there on the crowded floor.

I am grateful to monitor his
blood pressure out of the danger range.
and grateful he
does not start vomiting!

LUKE

I remember him at birth,
a wild thatch of dark hair
preceding his angry cry,
emerging from that tight tunnel.

Since, I have been present
at each exam,
each minor illness.

Today, I examine his
healthy little body in
preparation for his
entrance into kindergarten.

I place my stethoscope on
his wondering ears —
he listens to
his own heartbeat
with wide eyes and mouth.

And he giggles
as legs jerk
involuntarily
under my reflex hammer.

As he leaves, he turns
wistfully to his mom,
and asks —

"Mom, can boys be
doctors, too?"

MEGAN

She does not seem to be present.
From some faraway place,
she speaks, with vague voice,
eyes curiously unblinking,
skin pasty, dough-like.

I remember her as a spit-fire,
one who bridled at the
necessary bed-rest
during her troubled
pregnancies.

Now, she knows something
is not right, but lacks the
inner-fire to care. Yes,
her family has noticed
this descent into zombie-like
inactivity. Yes, she has trouble
keeping any thoughts going,
and prefers to sleep all the time.

She thinks it's been a year or more
since she felt herself, but
just thought she had become lazy.

I ask the questions her condition
brings to mind. Does she feel
cold, is she constipated, has she gained
weight, has her hair changed?

She answers a dull "yes" to all these
queries, and I know her likely
diagnosis, later confirmed by
lab tests. She has the most profound
hypothyroid state I have ever seen.

I don't know how much longer she
would have lived this slow death,
but I am so grateful such a
terrible state can be easily cured
by the daily swallowing of
one tiny pill.

A month later,
her eyes are clear,
her hair shiny,
her laugh easy,
her personality lively.

NANCY

I stand in my office with
the medical student,
his ready mind
straining to be filled
with the stuff of
the real medical world.

Among the things
I teach him —
listen hard to that
nagging little intuition, for
the pearl in its
insistent voice.

We next see Nancy,
new to my clinic.
Just a routine yearly
exam, no problems.
Well, actually, just
a heavy period last time.

All is normal,
quiet on exam,
no ripples in the
expected anatomy.

I hear my mouth
explain we need to
do a D&C, scrape
her uterus because
of that one heavy period.

She agrees.
In the hall,
my student is incredulous.
A D&C for that paltry
complaint?

At the D&C,
the scrapings prove to be malignant,
early — she is cured
by a hysterectomy.

Nancy will never know the
powerful teaching
she supplied for
a becoming doctor.

NETTIE

Nettie does not come
with her daughter today.
This is because she
is disruptive, hostile,
abusive, argumentative,
angry — and confused,
disoriented, forgetful,
depressed, deteriorating.

Her daughter, as caretaker,
is desperate for ideas
and relief. I listen
as she describes
Nettie's unforgiving
tongue, her demands
for daily attention, her refusal
to let any help in her
apartment, her slovenly
and filthy clothes.

She
needs to be listened to,
and know she has been heard.

The daughter lists all the
resources tried and failed,
and I list all the possible
resources yet to try.
Alzheimer's and Parkinson's
rage on — all Nettie's worst
personality characteristics
survive unchecked, while all
else slides.

And the daughter's own health begins
to fail — the burden is too much,
and she has been conscientious.
Her own daughter tells her —
"You're never going to get old, mother —
grandma's going to kill you."

I urge nursing home.
The daughter cannot
do this without
guilty conscience.
This good daughter,
though, will gradually
make this decision, as
I have planted the
endorsement seed.

BRUCE

The overhead asks for a doctor, stat.
I rush to the rear of the plane,
and find a flight attendant
on the floor, sweating, pale,
barely conscious.

I ask him questions
about his health
and learn he is an
Insulin dependent diabetic.

He has skipped a meal— too busy.
With his own glucometer
I learn his blood sugar is dangerously low.

The plane medical kit has
the correct injection he needs,
and he is provided orange juice.

We wait and watch as his skin dries,
his color returns, his blood sugar improves.
But he and I both know
he might tank again,
so every fifteen minute glucometer readings
must be done for a time.

Sure enough, though he has eaten by now,
he drops too low again.
Another injection fixes him for the duration of the flight.

In an hour, I see him busily providing
passenger service.

PATTY

This first pregnancy has been uneventful enough
just the ordinary complaints —
backache, heartburn,
swollen legs, hemorrhoids.

Today, as usual,
Patty reads a romantic
novel while she waits for me.

The cover
hints at steamy passion
within.

Patty is complaining today
of strong contractions.
I check her and find
her too early ripening,
threatening premature
delivery.

She will now have to spend time in bed,
flat, and perhaps will need medicine to prevent
that early appearance.

And I wonder, as I have often
wondered, about any
connection between reading sexy
novels and premature
contractions.
I've not yet seen any studies
regarding this possibility.

ROXANNE

Tattoos on
secret body places —
an everyday occurrence
in my office.

I like to hear their
stories, when, and why.

Roxanne's, new since
our last visit,
resides on her right breast.

It is crude, black anchor
with red heart overlay.
I ask its meaning, and why
it looks undone.

She tells me it isn't finished — should have
water, also.
I cannot picture how this
would improve it,
so ask its meaning.

"Well, then it would mean anchored in
a sea of love. But it hurt too much to
finish it. Besides, that boyfriend
isn't around anymore."

Sometimes it happens —
tattoos
live more permanent
than
love.

TERRENCE

The daughter, when she called,
seemed mildly concerned
that her dad, Terrence,
had not been out of bed for
five days. In fact, he had not been
very active or alert
for the three weeks since knee surgery.

Also, she told me,
he had fevers for most of these last days,
but now strangely
had a temperature
six degrees below
normal.

With these ominous symptoms,
I urged his immediate
evaluation in the
Emergency Room.

With a diagnosis of sepsis,
he arrived shortly after in
intensive care. Though
less than alert, he spoke
with a gentleness,
surprising since his life
had been made torture by
years of crippling and
deforming rheumatoid
arthritis.

His body dripped an
endless cold sweat,
and maintaining his
blood pressure, correcting
heart failure and sudden
onset of respiratory distress
and more and more ominous arrythmias

kept me steadily busy at
what became increasingly clear
was a hopeless task.

The antibiotics coursed through his veins,
but his kidneys, racked with
infection, were not working,
all his other systems closed down,
and after a few long hours,
the inevitable cardiac arrest
was final.

At autopsy, his operated knee, all internal organs,
and left shoulder were filled with the
aggressive staph infection that had
gone too far before he came for help.
In this era of potent antibiotics,
it is rare to see such devastating
infection.

I had not known this man
before our several hour struggle
together. In his dying, in that
painful dark slide, he
complained only a little about
the painful left shoulder.

Did he welcome the relief
from his many year struggle?
From the agony of twisted joints
and medicine complications?

I cannot know, nor can I know
how it happens I sometimes become the one
present at this most intimate
of passages. That it is an honor
and a sacred responsibility
I fully understand.

For always the release
into that next place
leaves behind certain
gifts for the living.

ANNIE

Though only fifteen,
she arrived alone
for all her
prenatal visits.

Her baby delivered quite
normally.
Alone, she was brave
and cooperative.

But then started
disastrous trouble.

The placenta
would not release,
and blood poured out
unceasingly.

I rushed with her to the operating room,
gave orders for emergency transfusions,
and, with deep examination,
learned, with dread,
her placenta
had grown into the
wall of the uterus.

I could not stop the tidal wave
of crimson flooding the floor.
First one surgeon arrived to help,
then a second.
In the end, she lost
her uterus-
at fifteen.

Twenty units of blood and surgery later
she is in critical but stable condition.

I locate her mother's phone number
and call her.
It is late night.

I explain her daughter has a
healthy son,
but is herself in critical condition, and
would she like to come in and be with her?

"She got herself into
this mess.
I'm going back to bed."

I make sure to sit with this child/mother
at least twice a day,
as she has no other visitors.

MARCIE

At 11:58 pm
She approached the
Emergency Room
Admissions desk.

The young Hispanic man,
working this job while he
completed his
Emergency Medical Training,
greeted her.

"Is it March 18?"
she asked.
Glancing at the clock,
he noted it would be
March 18 in two minutes.

"Yes, it is.
Can I help you?"

In a speedy motion,
she drew a long
kitchen knife
from her large
purse

and vigorously
plunged it deep
into her abdomen,
then dropped to the floor.

With his training,
he alerted the staff and me, just steps away,
through the door,
and he provided her all the correct
emergency care until we arrived.

After stabilization in the ER,
she was swiftly rolled
down the hall
to surgery.

She survived,
though with a bag on her
abdomen
to collect
her stool.

From the acute care hospital
she transferred to the first of
many long psychiatric
hospitalizations.

We all puzzled over
the idea of
committing suicide
at the Emergency Room
Registration desk.

LINEA

It was her yearly exam.
She had hypertension,
but otherwise, at sixty —
healthy.

She gave birth to
and nurtured
twelve children,
a beautiful family,
now all raised,
Mostly college graduates.
All on her husband's
teaching
salary.

Now, she says —
"I'm so depressed.
My life is over.
I have no value in the world."

I am astounded.
"Are you kidding?
Look at the wonderful
humans you guided and
gifted to the planet.
You are incredible!
What creativity and love
you possess."

She left my office,
went straight home,
and began to paint
and write poetry.

In that way she
reclaimed her smile
and her passion
for pouring joy
into others' lives.

CONNIE

Since surgery,
her doctor ignores
the six-month lingering
burning pain, pressure
and discharge.

She begins to doubt
the wisdom
of the hysterectomy.

But I know
what will be there
in a deeply hidden
vaginal recess.
Who can say why
her doctor ignores such
an easily healed problem?

Sure enough, there,
in the vaginal incision line,
lies the offending, angry red,
easily bleeding post-op
inflammatory polyp,
fngerling size,
troublemaker.

My simple and quick removal
will cure her discomfort.

As I do this,
I am reminded of the way
in which myths and fairy tales
are formed,
Drawing from real life
experience
as they do.

Do you remember the story of
the Princess and the Pea?

HANNAH

She is ninety-five
nearly comatose
after a fall and blow
to her head.

Scan shows large brain bleed
likely to be fatal, soon.
Usual action at this point
is to recommend compassionate care
in the hospital.

But daughter pleads for transfer and surgery.
She points out her mom's activity status
like that of a seventy-year-old.
Church choir, active on church committees,
volunteering in the community,
book clubs.

I am persuaded to call the neurosurgeon.
He is resistant, waste of money, no chance.
Finally, I persuade him,
then must persuade
the helicopter service.

She is transferred.
The next day her daughter calls me.
Mom had her surgery,
is sitting up in bed,
talking normally.

After two weeks at a rehab unit,
she returns home to her busy schedule.

This is a medical miracle.
Repayment for a life of service?

JOSEPHINE

The line of Haitians
of all ages and
myriad health problems
stretches around the building
and across the street.
Bodies are pressed tightly
front to back
as the line slowly
moves forward
in the merciless Haitian sun.

To entertain during the long wait,
my husband, Dmitri,
clowns, to their delight.

My scrubs soaked with sweat,
I will minister to 100 folks,
before the sun goes down.

Suddenly, a pregnant woman
in hard labor
is rushed in and laid on a wooden table.
Quick to examine, I see I will
be delivering a baby any moment.

And so I do — a lovely boy.
The family takes possession
of the placenta.

It must be buried at the door
to the family home.

Amid much chattering, excitement,
and laughter
they decide to name the infant
Dimitri, in honor of my husband.

For the next several years,
this little rascal
receives special presents
from us,
on each return of our medical mission.

His mom knew what she was doing
in his naming.

JOSHUA

I am teaching medical students
by example, as a family physician.

Joshua is attending a delivery with me,
his first.

When baby is safely on new mom's breast,
I begin the repair of her episiotomy.
Hoping to allow Joshua to place a few stitches,
I ask mom and dad for permission.

There is a brief pause.
Then mom leans up and asks,
"Did he take home economics?"

Another pause, then she laughs

MARY LOU

We are flying to Russia,
cramped in our airline seats.

The announcement asks urgently for a doctor.
I quickly respond.

In the flight attendant's bed compartments
I never knew existed,
I find a stricken, ashen, sweating woman,
complaining of crushing chest pain.
A quick exam confirms something dangerous —
either a heart attack or blood clot to the lungs.
I do what I can with the medicines available,
but say she must get to a hospital stat.

We are already over the Atlantic.
The plane must dump its fuel
as it is too heavy to land.

This done, the flight returns to Minneapolis.
Ambulance quick,
she is rushed to the hospital.

We are moved to first class!
I learn later she survives.
I am so very blessed
with doctor skills.

JACOB

At sixteen,
he means to die
from the rifle shot to his head.
But the muzzle,
placed vertically
under his chin,
directed the shot
through his face,
rather than His brain.

Called stat to the ER,
I find him alert,
with his face split in half,
eyes spared.

Once stable, the able
Ear, Nose, and Throat surgeon
begins the many hour, painstaking
process of piecing together
this ruined facial geography.

Jacob returns
from surgery
a swollen mass of tubes, wires, and sutures.
He heals steadily, until
only a few thin facial lines
remain to reveal
the story of that terrible day.

He finishes high school,
joins the work force,
marries.
I deliver three children into this family.

He never speaks of the "incident,"
and never reveals why.
A good therapist stabilized
his thinking and impulses.
For all his adult years
he lives a good life.
How fortunate —
his lousy aim.

JAMILAH

A refugee from Somali,
mother of five
struggling without a man,
Jamilah is considered,
by the staff,
to be crazy.

This is because she
is nearly a daily presence at the clinic
or Emergency Room,
often with an apparently
inconsequential complaint.

I have seen her a few times,
noted her desperate
wild eyed mannerisms.
She shuffles out after
each encounter,
perhaps soothed for a few moments.

One day, she asks for a
pelvic examination.
When she is undressed,
legs up in stirrups,
I am shocked speechless.

With horror, I see only a mass
of ugly scar tissue
where her labia and clitoris
would normally reside.

Once she is dressed,
we begin a discussion
about her sexual life.
It is hard for me not to cry
with her.

She tells me of the agony her parents
sent her into, at age seven, with crude
scraping away of all external femininity.
The brutal recovery period.
Her confusion about why this torture.

And now, she relates only pain
with any sexual expression.
No pleasure, ever.

"Please," she begs, "will you
do surgery and put me
back together?"

I see the reason for her
frequent visits.
If only I could help her.

MATHILDE

She is wiry, vigorous,
feisty, defiant
her yearly exam always an
occasion for mutual laughter.

Both her garden
and her life grow
rich and bountiful,
sprinkled with
the gorgeous fertility
of generous humor.

Today I see she is,
though another year older,
still in prime health.
Fluffy white hair and
loose skin suggests her age,
but steely muscles still
support an erect frame.

As I approach the pelvic part of her exam,
I discover her sparse private hair growth
Is dyed bright red.

She has been waiting for this.
In response to my questioning eyes,
she says, with double twinkle —

"My husband always wanted
to be married to a redhead!"

Elderly does not
properly define
this body and wit.

MARIA

Just beginning to sit up,
she is perpetual motion,
exploring glasses, rings,
stethoscope, everything
in her happy reach.

But her six-month
sunny face clouds
suddenly. Some
dawning realization
of my probing
frightens her.

At this point, I use
my foolproof cure for
six-month unhappiness —
I tear off a wad of crinkly exam
table paper and place
it directly in Maria's
wailing hands.

From there, the paper
whisks into her mouth,
and she calms down,
fascinated with the texture,
sound and apparently,
flavor of that silly paper.

I wonder each time if
I might strike it rich,
were I to invent edible
exam room paper,
perhaps in purple flavor,
or maybe red.

JENNY

Observation, listening
with all the senses —
tools made automatic
with repetitive use,
like walking or breathing.

Jenny, on our get-acquainted visit,
chats with me as
I examine her.

I learn where she works,
when her wedding will be,
how many guests are expected,
how long she's been engaged.

Finished, I write a prescription
for birth control pills,
and hand it to her.

She reads it, then stares at me
I don't' understand the look.

"But I didn't tell you I take
birth control pills. How did
you know this is the exact pill?"

I am reminded to make my leaps
of knowing
just a bit more smooth.

LAWRENCE

He seems a simple man,
Lawrence does.
His life appears uncluttered
by excessive learning.
Because his wife of forty
years has always been
an invalid,
There have been no children
cluttering up his energies.

But I suspect he is someone's favorite uncle.
Because his diabetes is unstable,
I see him often.

I always enjoy the easy
gentle smile that plays about his face.
He bears the difficulties of his life with contentment.

Today there is an impish grin
on his face.
An air of expectancy.
I review his lab tests,
Look at his home monitoring diary,
Check his vital signs,
Still the grin.

We talk about his health,
I adjust his insulin dose.
Then, I notice the
diamond earring, piercing
his left ear.

He follows my eyes,
and grins wide.

"My mother left me a pair of diamond earrings
when she died. I can't see why they should
just stay in the jewelry box."

I laugh with him and
compliment him on his unique style.

And I am aware he is wearing the true nature
of his heart on that proud ear.

GERTRUDE

On a sweaty August night,
I leave the hospital at three AM
after delivering
a new, noisy, squirmy little life.

Just outside,
in the not-light,
sits a woman dressed in
hospital gown, IV pole
standing sentinel.

I notice as the cigarette glow
flickers near her mouth.
Our eyes meet, hers near hidden
by thick night color,
but they flash defiance.

Whatever her illness,
whatever the cost,
whatever the inconvenience
or embarrassment,
she WILL smoke.

Addiction,
that swimming in
dark, dangerous water,
eventually seduces,
then drowns
the spirit,
caught off guard
while answering
the call from
below.

ABIGAIL

Though young, she
at 370 pounds
breaths ancient,
with wheezes and whistles.

For her rheumatoid arthritis,
she daily swallows several
powerful double-edged swords,
and sweats spirit-blood
in her misery.

As I speak with smiling assurance
of new ways in which
altering her specific diet
will bring healing.
I see her pasty skin
sprout angry spikes,
poison darts,
shooting at me,
to still my offending mouth.

"I will not live long,
and you would deprive me of
my only pleasure,"
say clenched teeth and teary eyes.

I understand —
my words of hope have been
received as threat and attack.

The barbed-wire barrier
firmly in place,
we part,
each of us
frustrated.

TINA

I try to deny the gray
fluffing the fringes of
my own head.
I am often, these days
confronted with those
grown-up images of
the babies I once delivered.

Tina, now twenty-one, is here today
for her first OB visit.
She was entering kindergarten
when last I saw her.

Now she's a big boned
firmly packed young woman,
grinning with her four-month
pregnant tummy.

I ask what she's doing these days —
college, perhaps, or work? I notice she
is unmarried, and still living in
our small town.

She gives me a strange look —
I am not sure why.
I wait.
Then she tells me she is a dancer.
This information surprises me, a bit,
as she is not exactly built like
most dancers, so I ask her
what type of dance.

With another strange look,
she takes a deep breath and,
somewhat defensively tells me —
"I am an exotic dancer."

She declines to reveal where she
does this dancing, but informs
me that now she only dances behind
glass, so she doesn't have to see her
customers. I believe she tells me this
to reassure me.

I ask what she will do for work
when her tummy gets big which will be in another
few weeks. She cheerfully tells me
of a friend who performed all the way through
her eighth month by keeping her backside to
her customers.

This creates an interesting picture
for me, and I cannot help but
try to imagine the thought
process of patrons watching a naked,
eight-month pregnant woman
strip, bump and grind.

When I examine her, I find her
shaved clean of pelvic hair.
This will be a help to the obstetrics nurses.
And those same nurses will probably
find the tattoo interesting that
sits over her pubis.

She sports, in this private spot,
a pair of vivid Mick Jagger lips
with a long, lascivious
tonging hanging out, and
the word "Lickable"
crowning the scene.

A doctor knows, of course,
those little newborn souls
package a life with
limitless potential.
Sometimes, the direction that potential
bounces is stunning in
its creative surprises.

JIMMY AND JOHNNY

I delivered these twins
after an uneventful pregnancy.
They were healthy, mostly.

Active toddlers of three,
they played in the driveway one day,
and Dad backed out of the garage,
the car fatally crushing Jimmy.

Mom or Dad, a year later,
decided to fill an empty
pop can with gasoline
For later use outside,
then left it on the coffee table.
Johnny drank it.
We could not save him.

Maybe life in this family
was too difficult,
and these two cherubs
decided to leave.

ED

Ed raged against
his looming dark night
for years.
while emphysema,
cancer, stroke, and congestive
heart failure ravaged, savaged,
eroded will.

To keep his fragile body
functioning
required exquisite balance of
medicines,
meticulous
monitoring.

This is why I saw him
with his wife
every few weeks
for years,

until he died.

And this is why I
always had a fresh
supply of dirty jokes.

He got them from his
priest

So always, before each
leave-taking, we laughed
together over the latest story,
passed to me like a precious
jewel.

This is why even on his
deathbed
we laughed, though he
labored hopelessly at breathing,
his cold hand grasping mine.

Today, Clarice, his widow,
scolds me for being behind schedule.
She is rested now, from her
long nursing siege.
Ed was quite a challenge,
not always in a kindly mood.

So, Clarice grumps at me.
Her life is waiting
out there,
let's get this exam over with.

On my way out the door, she says —
"Oh, doc, did you hear the one about
Miss Pussy Green?
My priest told it to me."

FLORINDA

"It's not enough to
be a survivor,"
she said,
"you have to get
beyond that stage, as well,
else you're still identified
with that victim-self."

Torn up, broken —
that's the ongoing condition
of her body.
Born of an alcoholic prostitute,
witness, at three,
to her uncle's shotgun suicide,
sold into prostitution by age eight.
Sexually abused by her therapist,
veteran of countless
psychiatric hospitalizations
and rapes,
with wrists and chest bearing
tangled white scars,
at least twice near fatally beaten.
Then, married and
sexually abused some more
by a powerful
church
authority figure.

So she became many,
coping in that way
with the unending pain
and shame.

And she learned to cling
with tenacity to
the slender, temporary
lifelines
that occasionally
dangled.

From that bleak cauldron
emerged
a magnificent therapist,
spilling hope and healing
to dying children
and their families.

Today, I examine her,
in preparation for the last of
the many surgeries
repairing her damaged
pelvis.

Even without a stethoscope,
I hear her spirit
SOAR.

To know Florinda is to experience the
true nature
of alchemy.
From the fiery conjunction of the
basest elements
flows
the purest gold.

JESSICA

This has been a normal labor and delivery —
not a first child, so slid on out
in speedy style.

But who among us can begin to know
how this young mother
can feel,
tears splashing silently
on solemn lips
as she gazes at this latest miracle.

What does it mean for her to contemplate this
carrying forward of the stuff of
a young man and a young woman's vitality?
Two who loved each other,
and created in joy
this next life.

How can a young woman,
in the midst of this joy,
in the seventh month of pregnancy,
register the sudden cardiac death
of that vital young father?

She will raise this child
without him.
This was not her plan in life,
there were other plans
that brightened her
days.

But women have,
bred into their genetics,
always understood,
in that place where
such things are only whispered
behind closed thoughts,
that their man may not be there
to help raise his child.
And she will go on.
From the future,
her child tugs her forward.

JUDY

In one of those fortunate misfortunes,
her fall in the bathtub and resultant
breast bruise led to my discovery of
the first breast lump. It was cancer,
and that breast was removed.

Some years later, the other breast
went the same way, so that now
she wears false breasts in her bra,
to restore her womanly shape.

She seems victorious in this battle
with breast cancer. It is now over ten
years since the last bout.

Today her visit is a routine yearly exam.
Summer has been cool,
but yesterday was blistering hot.
I ask her how she liked the heat.

With her characteristic good nature,
she tells me,
"It was so hot,
I had to take my boobs off!"

No one can say why one individual
gets cancer, and cancer again,
then survives. I have no doubt,
though, that this gift
of humor and laughter
makes a difference, and tips
the scales favorably.

JOE AND SALLY

Over the years,
I have participated deeply
in the troubles
and joys of this family.
Her infertility, traced to his lack of sperm,
resolved into two pregnancies by donor insemination.
Both, though complicated by obesity, diabetes, and
hypertension —
ended successfully with C-Section deliveries.

I have seen these two children flourish
over the last three years —
lively toddlers now,
healthy, clear eyed.

All of these events
of a man and woman's life together
funnel down to this
electric point in time,
this super-charged moment.

Now, as these two sit before me,
I must say terrible words.

The test is positive.
He has active AIDS.
I know he is not surprised.
He has been losing weight,
suffering fevers, swollen glands.
I know he carries a heavy secret.

But first I must explore the range of damage.
Blood is drawn from these toddlers,
from this stunned wife.

And I will check records on the semen donor.
My lab techs, semen analyzers,
will need to be tested.

I hope I will not need to inform the operating room,
the nursery, and the post-partum floor
of exposure to HIV positive blood.

For now I will provide resources, counseling,
referrals, support groups.

In every life, disaster patiently waits
behind the most fragile curtain.

KATHY, DARREN, AND LITTLE JULIE

Darren, the thoughtful big brother,
entertains sweet Julie, while I
talk with their mother.
These children play a game
of post office. One writes
on paper, then brings it to the other,
at the "post office" to mail it.
It is creative, and I am distracted from their
mother's concerns as they embellish and giggle.

Darren, at eight, is mature, though impish.
He has, perhaps, not had as much attention
since Julie's arrival, four years ago,.
We had not expected her tortuously
twisted, lifeless limbs —
there'd been no clue during pregnancy.

Kathy massaged those arms, legs,
worked them, moved them.
Slowly, through many hip
and foot surgeries, Julie developed function,
began to feed herself with weak, splinted hands.
Next she rolled about on the floor,
then sat, then stood.
Finally, in braced legs,
she walks about,
wobbly at first,
but steadily improving.

Bright, charming,
she does keep progressing.

But Kathy has begun to suffer from
constant lifting. Her neck
plagues with toothache pain,
her back as well. She needs respite,
healing, and attention.
She requires a listening ear.
She does not complain of her lot,
nor of Julie's disabilities.

She just needs some help for a little while.

We talk, lay out plans for
her healing, laugh a bit.

When I leave, but still
in hearing range,
Darren says,
"Mom! Dr. Jan's sure got lots of
gray hair!"

I laugh. Kathy is mortified.

Cheeky eight-year-old minds
and mouths are always
good for the unexpected
comic relief.

LARRY

He comes,
too early bent of neck,
stiff of back.
Blue terror lurks
not so hidden behind
still young eyes.
Wasted hands
plead the case.

"Oh yes, the feet do hurt,
but yesterday I biked
twenty miles,
played a full
round of golf.
That right ankle
always swells
like that."

There will be exercises,
soothing medicines,
supplements and herbs that
will help some.

For now, as he struggles to
lift his face,
fixed to the ground
by treacherous neck-curve,
I lock those blue eyes,
engage the terror,
walk along that slippery path.

There, in the heartbeat
synapse of that gaze,
flows the healing.

MELINDA

We knew it would be twins.
Though only sixteen, her
pregnancy progressed
without any glitches.

But there is risk
with twins.
even with both babies head down
I elect to deliver her in the operating room,
in case of emergency C-Section.

It is December 31, 1992, 11:55 pm.
Baby number one arrives
lusty, blond little girl.

But immediately baby two is in trouble
as the umbilical cord
has emerged first,
creating crisis to blood flow for the infant.

I must reach up and
push baby out of the birth canal
to get pressure off the cord,
and keep holding the child back,
until the surgeon arrives
and performs the C-Section.

Baby number two arrives at 00:08,
January 1, 1993.
He is lively, healthy,
with dark skin and black hair.

So this young lady has managed
to have twins with
birthdays on different days,
in different years
and varying dramatically
in appearance.

The universe enjoys
a good prank
at times.

RICKY

The police and EMTs
escort him in, strapped to a gurney, struggling
and screaming nonsensically.

He is clearly high on some drug.
In this area, at this time,
the drug most likely to
create this level of craziness
is K2, or bath salts.

His drug screen is negative,
ruling out methamphetamine.
I sedate him, he babbles
for a few hours,
then sleeps for four hours.
When he awakes, he
is lucid and polite.

So, after seven hours in the ER,
I release him to home.

One hour later the incoming gurney
again contains a raving Ricky.
This time with a six-inch laceration to his forehead.
He thought it a good idea to put his head
through a closed window.

After the same sedation and rest,
I repair his wound.

Some days later administration
receives a complaint
that he should not have been
allowed to return home the first time
to take more K2.

I understand parents' desperation,
but also know they must come to
understand the concept
of enabling.

SHIRLEY

Newlywed, nineteen, bright future.
She sits in the
passenger seat
on a short excursion.
New husband drives.
Sunny, warm day.

Passing car has a canoe tied on top.
It slips its bonds
and flies directly at her,
crashing through the front window and
lodging in her skull.

Though tragically damaged,
she survives
with skills of a five-year-old.

Husband labors, for years,
to teach simple cooking,
easy home chores.
but she is not able
to read, or enjoy most movies.
Her conversation is simple, slow,
innocent.

He tells me of yearning for a family.
I do not hold hope for her to
raise a child.

Even so, she becomes pregnant.
She does not understand
her body changes.

We try with a baby doll
to prepare her in some way.
In labor, she is terrified and
pitifully begs us
to stop hurting her.

Her perfect little boy is placed in her arms.
At first confused,
a sea change washes over her.
She cuddles appropriately,
and takes the babe to her breast
like a fully competent woman.

Over the years, she demonstrates
a completely intact
mothering instinct.
With help, she and husband raise
the joy of their lives,
their miracle boy,
who proved that even a canoe cannot
remove that precious, primitive urge.

RHONDA

It is yearly exam time,
she is a many-year patient.

I take her history —
feeling fine.
Her exam is normal, too.

As she sits on the exam table,
completely swathed in
paper sheet and gown,
we have end of the visit conversation.

This discussion tips topsy,
when completely off the subject
she asks if I would like to be her special friend.
I understand from her body language
and unusual format of her question —

She is inviting me into a sexual relationship.
This is a first in my exam rooms.

With a few exceptions,
I have not had any kind
of Personal friendship
with a current patient.
Let alone this suggestion.

I am kind in my definite "no,"
and once again,
I realize I will never see or hear
all possible situations
in my profession.

JENNIFER

She is here again,
every Wednesday.
She has a psychiatric disorder,
undiagnosed.
She refuses to see
a psychiatrist.

Instead, she angrily stalks
into my office every week,
demanding soothing words
and gentle direction.

Of course her life is messy.
She seems to think this is my fault.
She scowls at me throughout
the visit.

I admit I groan when I see her name
on my appointment list.
She appears to hate me,
even murderously so.

And yet, here she is,
every week.

One night I came home to my
secluded country dwelling,
to find her standing, partially hidden,
in the woods.

I felt fear, and called the sheriff.
He picked her up without incident.
The next day I dictate the letter
releasing her as my patient,
providing many options for her care.

I don't ever see her again, but
find myself wary for
some years.

GLORIA

She is in her 80's.
Still walking 2 miles a day.
Today is her yearly visit.

She is in good spirits,
All is fine.
No complaints.

On exam, I find an ugly, green-aging bruise
on her left rib cage.
And no breath sounds in her left lung.

"Oh, that bruise. I fell on the fence
2 weeks ago."

X-ray confirms a completely collapsed
lung and a chest cavity
filled with blood.

Have you been walking every day — 2 miles?
"Sure I have, why not?
Is something wrong?"

This is one tough lady.
I elect to let nature
cure the problem,
and do not place any tubes.

2 weeks later —
50% improved.
2 more weeks, X-ray clear.

Good attitude,
good genetics,
good life habits.
Miracle healing.

MARILYN

I thought I had a good
new doctor, she said.
I was worried about the
upcoming major surgery.
He was so highly recommended.

He briskly outlined
the procedure.
He seemed disinclined to discuss
possible complications.
I told him I would be praying for a
good outcome.

He told me, "Your God isn't going
to help you.
Only my skills."

She found another
surgeon.

ABOUT THE AUTHOR

Dr. Jan was blessed to have a forty-seven-year career in medicine — twenty-seven years in family medicine, practicing womb to tomb needs, and delivering over 3,000 babies. Following that, time in Urgent Care, Hospitalist, and eight years in Emergency Medicine. She treasures these years and misses the patients and staff deeply.

Throughout her career, she also pursued humanitarian goals — clowning in many countries and refugee camps with Dr. Patch Adams, and providing medical care to unserved multitudes in many countries, including Haiti, Argentina, and Nepal. She developed and managed a charity and art gallery for the benefit of Russian orphans.

Meanwhile, she squeezed in time to create hundreds of published articles covering holistic medicine and mind/body/spirit issues. In addition, Dr. Jan continued her love of music with a total of fifty years as a church organist. In retirement, she continues her interests in music, art, and writing, especially story telling.

Each of these mini-stories was gifted to her as the jewels of life experienced in the doctor/patient connection of healing.

Previous books include *Football Wife: Coming of Age with the NFL*, and inclusion in three anthologies, *In The Words Of Olympic Peninsula Authors* Volumes 1, 2, and 3. All available on Amazon.

Dr. Jan lives in Port Angeles, Washington, with her husband and three cats. She may be contacted at jantadams@aol.com

ALSO FROM THIS AUTHOR

FOOTBALL WIFE
Coming of Age with the NFL

"As a doctor, I decided to write and publish *Football Wife* ... reflecting from a position of knowledge on my decade of

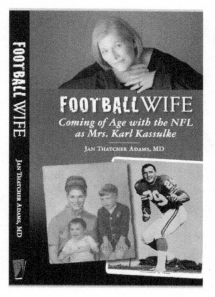

memories good and bad — not just a kiss-and-tell book. Instead it looks at real, timeless issues that played out for me in a very public arena."
— Jan Thatcher Adams MD, author.

"Jan Adams provides an insightful look into a hidden world, as well as a cautionary tale of the trappings of the most popular "game" in America."
— Christopher Nowinski, author of *Head Games: Footballs Concussion Crisis*

Available through Amazon.

Made in the USA
Monee, IL
17 October 2020

45375910R00069